REALISTIC

TATTOOS

COLORING BOOK
FOR ADULTS

MODERN TATTOO DESIGNS FOR ADULT RELAXATION:
SUGAR SKULLS, PHOENIX, FLOWERS, DRAGON, AND MORE

TattooTribes Press

© 2022 Roberto Gemori.

ISBN-13: 978-88-942056-9-5

ISBN-10: 88-942056-9-X

All tattoos in this book are original images by TattooTribes

Bonus image from *Polynesian Tattoos: 42 Modern Tribal Designs to Color and Explore* by Roberto Gemori © 2018
Reprinted in arrangement with Shambhala Publications, Inc. Boulder, CO.

35+ MODERN TATTOOS
TO COLOR IN OR INK

crafted by the artists of TattooTribes with passion and attention to detail, to give you that "moment-out-of-time" feeling that will help you shut the world out for a while.

1 MONTH of FREE DESIGNS

TattooTribes is known for the quality of its works, coming from over 20 years designing tattoos. That's why our *Monday Tattoos* service, before becoming popular with coloring book fans alike, has been a source of inspiration for many tattoo artists around the world.
Would you like to download 8 to 10 additional FREE designs? Follow the link, and enjoy ONE full FREE MONTH of *Monday Tattoos* (presently 3$/month) + the PDF of this book!

https://coloringbook.pictures/weekly.html

FOREWORD

Each design explores a different theme among some of the most celebrated and loved in the world of tattoos: sugar skulls, dragon, phoenix, flowers, cobra, Balinese demon, deer, samurai, geisha, Poseidon, Medusa—all with a twist, and the list goes on!

Nature is often incorporated as a decorative element for its beauty and soothing power. From the classic beauty of the rose, to the exotic aesthetic of the lotus, the hibiscus, and the Japanese peony, and the simple beauty of poppies, flowers often make the perfect match or contrasting element for the main designs.

Why 35 **PLUS**?

Because there's a small surprise at the end— (and some more when you follow the Bonus link.)

4

Did you enjoy this book?
Would you leave your honest review on Amazon?

Your opinion means a lot to us,
and your feedback will be much appreciated!

More books from TattooTribes:

Polynesian Tattoo Designs (2014)
Vol.1 - Ocean Legacy

A large-format book collecting all 93 Polynesian-styled tattoo designs from design books numbers 1, 2, 3, and 4, each one accompanied by its stencil: Mantas, Turtles, Sharks, and Sealife.

Polynesian Tattoos (2018)
42 Modern Tribal Designs to Color and Explore

A coloring book for adults featuring 42 original tattoos, each one accompanied by a description of its meanings.

The Big Book of Small Tattoos - Vol. 1 (2019)
400 Small Tattoos for Women and Men

Whether you are approaching tattoos for the first time and want to start small, or you're a longtime fan and only have just that tiny little spot left, you will appreciate this book and its philosophy: small and meaningful.

The Big Book of Small Tattoos - Vol. 2 (2021)
200+ Small Polynesian Tattoos

Each small to minimal design is a statement, embodying an aspect or trait from the Pacific islands, and carrying a memory of palm trees, sun, thriving ocean life, and sandy beaches.

The Big Book of Small Tattoos - Vol. 0 (2021)
100+ Unalomes & One-Line Minimalistic Tattoos

Can a small tattoo be deeply meaningful? The unalome proves it beyond doubt.
But what are unalomes? What do they represent? Is it right for you to get one? What is the best placement? Find the answers and 100+ designs in this book.

The Polynesian Tattoo Handbook (2011)
Practical Guide to Creating Meaningful Polynesian Tattoos

Learn Polynesian tattoos and their symbolism. 250+ pages with symbols, their meanings, their placement on the body, case studies, and step-by-step tattoo creation, basic elements, and reusable designs.

The Polynesian Tattoo Handbook, Vol. 2 (2018)
An In-Depth Study of Polynesian Tattoos and of Their Foundational Symbols

Unpacking the five main Polynesian styles: Samoan, Marquesan, Tahitian, Hawaiian, and Maori. 206 pages, 550+ illustrations, 400+ symbols and variants.

**AND DON'T FORGET YOUR FREE GIFTS: 8 BONUS IMAGES
AND THE PDF VERSION OF THIS BOOK**
to print its designs how many times you like:

https://coloringbook.pictures/weekly.html

A final SURPRISE
('cause we also love to overdeliver)
A BONUS DESIGN from our coloring book *Polynesian Tattoos*
Enjoy!

Made in United States
North Haven, CT
14 April 2023

35433924R00046